Astrolo... Book

Color Your Zodiac Sign

The 12 Signs

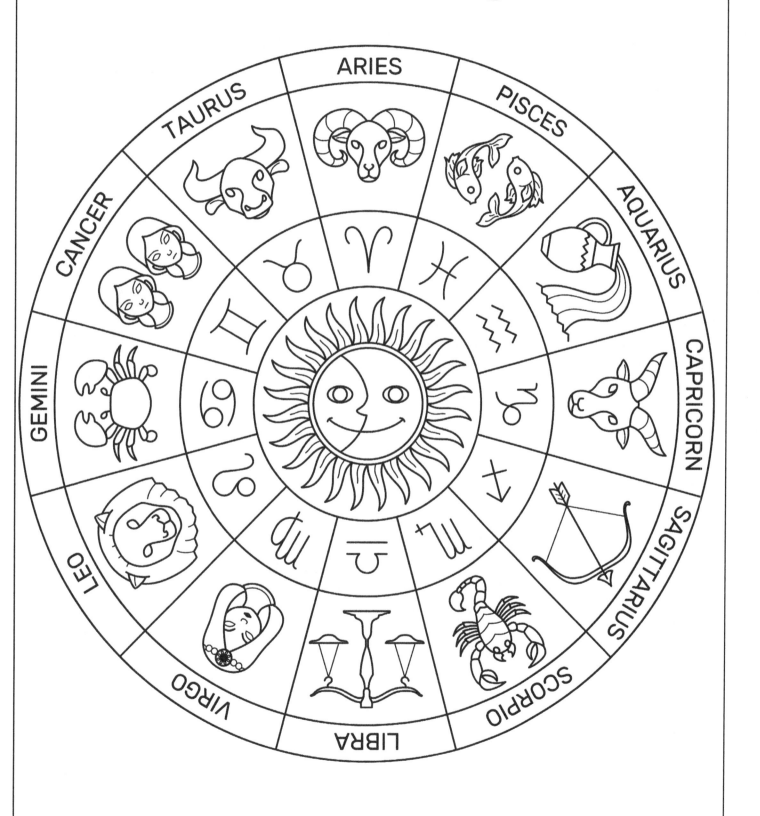

Sign Symbols

ARIES

TAURUS

GEMINI

CANCER

LEO

VIRGO

LIBRA

SCORPIO

SAGITTARIUS

CAPRICORN

AQUARIUS

PISCES

Taurus

April 20 - May 20

TAURUS IS AN EARTH sign, represented by the bull. Ruled by Venus—the planet which governs love, beauty, and money—they are extremely infatuated with all things luxurious. Both material and non-material wealth are very important to them. Their strengths include patience, devotion, stability, and loyalty. The Taurus highly values aesthetic beauty and therefore generally have immaculate taste in everything from food to décor. Like their spirit animal, the bull, however, they are known to be very stubborn and adverse to change. Still, as an earth sign, Taurus are practical and the voice of reason in any chaotic situation.

Symbol: Bull

Planet: Venus

Element: Earth

Colors: Pink, Green

Traits: Reliable, Practical, Loyal, Stubborn, Possessive

Constellation:

TAURUS

TAURUS

Taurus

TAURUS

TAURUS

TAURUS

Taurus

Taurus

♉ Taurus

Made in the USA
Middletown, DE
15 March 2023

26839944R00044